"YOU KNOW..."

PORT TALLON
Welcomes
Careful Drivers

"...LIFE IN THE
SLOW LANE."

WHAT *IS* IT THAT MAKES US WHAT WE *ARE*?

WHAT IS IT THAT *DEFINES* US? IS IT WHERE WE *LIVE*? IS IT OUR *SCHOOLING*?

OR IS IT OUR *FAMILY*?

ALEX RIDER.

FAMILY. HAVE YOU *PREPARED* SOMETHING FOR US?

OH! UM... YES.

COME ON, THEN.

GO ON.

YEAH.

OK.

I DIDN'T EVEN **KNOW** MY PARENTS. THEY **DIED** WHEN I WAS SMALL. I LIVE WITH MY **UNCLE**, AND HE'S NOT THERE MUCH **EITHER**.

THERE'S NOT MUCH I CAN **SAY** ABOUT MY FAMILY.

I HAVE A SORT OF HOUSEKEEPER INSTEAD, BECAUSE HE'S ALWAYS AWAY ON **BUSINESS**.

CORNWALL

"HE'S GOT A REALLY **BORING JOB**."

"HE'S A **BANK SUPERVISOR**. HE'S IN CHARGE OF **CUSTOMER CARE**."

BOOM!

BRAKKA

RI D3R

"I WOULDN'T SAY *I* WAS MUCH LIKE HIM..."

BEETHOVEN
DISC 3 02:56

BEEP

WHIRRRR

KLIK!

FRONT MISSILE LAUNCH
REAR MISSILE LAUNCH
EJECTOR SEAT

FRONT MISS

TARGET LOCKED

REA MISSI

DIT

DIT

DIIIIIIII...

"...AND I DON'T THINK ANYONE *MAKES* US WHAT WE ARE."

"I THINK WE JUST *ARE*."

THE NEW **STORMBREAKER**

YOUR SCHOOL WILL HAVE ONE SOON

THAT WAS *REALLY SAD* ABOUT HAVING NO MOM AND DAD, ALEX.

YOU'RE SUCH A *LOSER!*

WHY DON'T YOU JUST *GET LOST,* GARY?

BULLIES ARE SO... *LAST YEAR.*

HEY, SABINA.

OH...

HI, ALEX.

I WAS **WONDERING**... DO YOU WANT TO **DO** SOMETHING THIS WEEKEND?

NO.

I MEAN, **I CAN'T**.

I HAVE **RIDING LESSONS** ON SATURDAY, AND THEN I'M GOING **OUT** WITH MY MOM AND DAD.

OH!

SORRY...

IT DOESN'T MATTER.

MAYBE **NEXT** WEEKEND!

WHATEVER.

BEEP BEEP

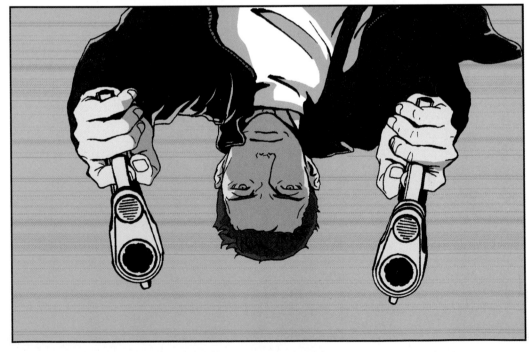

STORMBREAKER

ANTHONY HOROWITZ

Adapted by Antony Johnston

Illustrated by
Kanako Damerum
& Yuzuru Takasaki

SCHOLASTIC INC.
New York   Toronto   London   Auckland
Sydney   New Delhi   Hong Kong

HE *NEVER* LET ME COME IN HERE.

I DIDN'T *REALLY* KNOW *ANYTHING* ABOUT HIM.

HE WAS MY *ONLY* FAMILY, JACK.

WHAT AM I GOING TO *DO*?

IAN RIDER WAS A *GOOD* MAN. EVERYONE WHO WORKED WITH HIM WILL *REMEMBER* HIS *COURAGE*, AND HIS *LOYALTY*.

HE WAS, ABOVE ALL, A *TRUE* PATRIOT.

PATRIOT?

FORASMUCH AS IT HATH **PLEASED** ALMIGHTY GOD, OF HIS GREAT **MERCY**...

WHIRRR...

...TO TAKE **UNTO** HIMSELF THE SOUL OF OUR DEAR BROTHER HERE **DEPARTED**...

DID YOU **MEAN** WHAT YOU **SAID**? ABOUT LOOKING **AFTER** ME?

OF **COURSE** I DID! COME ON, YOU **KNOW** I WOULDN'T LEAVE YOU. ANYWAY, WHO **ELSE** IS THERE?

I'VE BEEN **LIVING** WITH YOU FOR **NINE YEARS**. HOW MUCH **MORE** RELATED DO YOU WANT TO BE?

BUT WILL YOU BE **ALLOWED** TO? I MEAN, WE'RE NOT EVEN **RELATED**.

WAS IT JUST **ME**, OR WAS THERE SOMETHING ABOUT THOSE **BANKERS** THAT STRUCK YOU AS **WEIRD**?

JACK---!

! HEY THAT'S ALL **IAN'S** STUFF! WHAT ARE YOU **DOING**?

HEY!

BROOOOO...

JEFF SLATER
AUTO WRECKERS
HEAVEN FOR CARS

SOUTH LONDON

HEY!

YOU SEEN *NIGEL*?

NAH.

WELL, IF YOU *SEE* HIM, TELL HIM I *WANT* HIM.

WEIRD.

DOESN'T **LOOK** LIKE IT WAS IN A CRASH AT **ALL**...

THE **RIDER** CAR SHOULD HAVE BEEN DONE **TWO DAYS** AGO.

SO DO IT **NOW**, ALL RIGHT?

BUT I DIDN'T GET THE *PAPERWORK*...

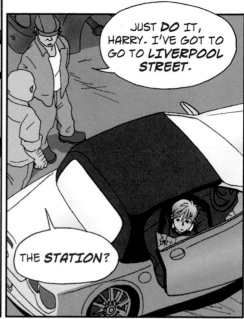

JUST *DO* IT, HARRY. I'VE GOT TO GO TO *LIVERPOOL STREET*.

THE *STATION*?

WHERE *ELSE*, YOU BERK? I'M TAKING THEM THE *STUFF*...

WOW...

SKREEEEEEE

WHAT—?

?

CHELSEA

AAAAAAAAAAA

KER— —CHUNK!

GOOD MORNING, ALEX. SHOULDN'T YOU BE AT SCHOOL?

I ... WAS ... ON THE PLATFORM AT LIVERPOOL STREET... AND NOW I'M HERE...

THAT'S RIGHT.

SO WHAT IS THIS PLACE?

HOGWARTS?

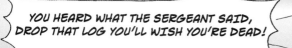

YOU HEARD WHAT THE SERGEANT SAID, DROP THAT LOG YOU'LL WISH YOU'RE DEAD!

...AND SO WE'LL DO IT ALL AGAIN!

WE DON'T LIKE THIS, WE'RE IN PAIN...

BRECON BEACONS, WALES

ON YOUR **FEET!**

GENTLEMEN, THIS IS OUR LATEST **RECRUIT.** HE'S HERE FOR **TWO WEEKS' TRAINING.**

DON'T **ASK** ME ABOUT IT, BECAUSE **I** DON'T KNOW A THING. I JUST DO WHAT I'M **TOLD.**

WE HAVE NO **NAMES** HERE, NO **RANKS.** THIS IS **K UNIT.**

FOX.

BEAR.

EAGLE.

WOLF.

AND

YOU'LL BE **CUB.**

SOMEBODY GET HIM A **BED.**

HFF

HFF

KEEP THAT GUN ABOVE YOUR HEAD...

GBBL RGBR LRGR GLBR GR GL LBRGR!

BRECON BEACONS

YOU'RE NOT IN THE *PLAYGROUND* NOW, CUB! *MOVE IT!*

LET ME GIVE YOU A *HAND*, CUB.

NO, WAI...T!

AAAAAAAAH

BLOOP!

HAHAHA!

HAHAHA HAHA!

HAHAHAHA!

KIYAAA!

KRASH

THERE'S A **FIREPLACE.**

HOW DID **YOU** KNOW?

I SAW THE **CHIMNEY** ON THE WAY IN.

THE KID'S RIGHT. IT'S **CLEAR.**

YOU CAN'T. YOU'RE TOO BIG.

YEAH, **RIGHT.** YOU THINK THEY'D JUST **LEAVE** IT IF THEY THOUGHT WE COULD ALL CLIMB **UP?**

WE DON'T **TRUST** HIM.

WHY NOT?

WELL, WE DON'T TRUST **ANYONE**. IT'S SORT OF WHAT WE'RE **FOR**.

FORTU

Inside
Darrius Sayle

KLIK

WE ALWAYS **THOUGHT** DARRIUS SAYLE WAS TOO **GOOD** TO BE **TRUE**. SO, SIX MONTHS AGO, WE SENT AN AGENT TO KEEP AN **EYE** ON HIM.

YOU MEAN MY **UNCLE**.

YES.

SAYLE HAS A **MANUFACTURING PLANT** IN **CORNWALL**, BUILT ON TOP OF WHAT USED TO BE A **TIN MINE**. IAN RIDER WENT THERE AS A **SECURITY GUARD**...

...AND HE **FOUND** SOMETHING. IN HIS LAST MESSAGE TO US, HE MENTIONED A **VIRUS**.

A **COMPUTER VIRUS**...?

WE DON'T KNOW. HE WAS ON HIS WAY TO **TELL** US, BUT HE NEVER ARRIVED.

SOMETHING'S GOING ON. WE NEED TO GET SOMEONE **IN** THERE TO TAKE A LOOK **AROUND**,

AND THIS MAY BE OUR **LAST CHANCE**.

DISK DRIVE WORLD

COMPETITION WINNER
Kevin Blake

WHY *ME?*

THIS IS *KEVIN BLAKE*, A COMPUTER NERD. SIX WEEKS AGO HE WON A *COMPETITION* IN THIS MAGAZINE.

EVER *READ* IT?

THE *FIRST PRIZE* WAS A *VISIT* TO CORNWALL AND A CHANCE TO TRY OUT THE *STORMBREAKER.*

HE'S DUE TO ARRIVE *TOMORROW.*

...

I'LL SHOW YOU.

IT'S A *PR STUNT.* I IMAGINE MR. SAYLE IS TRYING TO SHOW THE WORLD WHAT A *NICE MAN* HE IS. GET A *KIDDY* IN TO SEE THE WORKS.

YOU'LL TAKE KEVIN'S PLACE.

BUT I'M NOTHING *LIKE* HIM.

DISK DRIVE WORLD

COMPETITION WINNER
Kevin Blake

WE'VE SPOKEN TO THE *EDITOR.*

!!

THERE'S JUST ONE **PROBLEM**...

I DON'T KNOW ANYTHING **ABOUT** COMPUTERS. I'M **NOT** A NERD.

BUT YOU SOON **WILL** BE.

WE ONLY HAVE **THREE DAYS** LEFT. THERE'S A LAUNCH AT THE **SCIENCE MUSEUM** NEXT FRIDAY. **70,000** STORMBREAKER COMPUTERS GOING LIVE...

...

WE **DON'T** WANT YOU TO GET INTO ANY **TROUBLE**, ALEX. JUST TAKE A LOOK **AROUND**. AND BE CAREFUL OF SAYLE. HE MAY **SEEM** CHARMING...

...BUT HE'S ABOUT AS CHARMING AS A **SNAKE**.

JUST KEEP YOUR **EYES** OPEN AND REPORT **BACK**.

BUT HOW WILL I DO **THAT**?

WE'LL SUPPLY YOU WITH A **TELECOMMUNICATIONS DEVICE**. THAT AND...

OTHER GADGETS.

I GET **GADGETS**?

I KEEP MY **SPECIAL TOYS** DOWN HERE.

SOMEWHERE CHILDREN **AREN'T** ALLOWED, I'M RATHER PLEASED TO SAY...

HERE WE ARE.

LET'S START WITH **THIS.**

A **YO-YO?** THAT'S A LITTLE **OLD-FASHIONED...**

ON THE CONTRARY, IT'S...

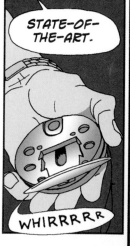

STATE-OF-THE-ART.

WHIRRRRR

A **MINIATURIZED ENGINE** WITH **TRACTION POWER** UP TO NINETY POUNDS.

THE MAIN BODY IS **MAGNETIC,** AND THE CORD IS A SPECIALLY DEVELOPED FORM OF **SUPERNYLON.** IT COMES WITH **BATTERIES** INCLUDED, AND A YEAR'S **GUARANTEE.**

AND HERE'S SOMETHING TO **PUT IT IN.**

OH,

RIGHT...

FOUNTAIN PEN.

NOT USED BY MANY YOUNG PEOPLE THESE DAYS, ALAS...

A *MODIFIED NINTENDO DS.* WHAT IT DOES DEPENDS ON THE *CARTRIDGE* THAT YOU PLACE IN IT.

THE *NIB* CAN BE FIRED FROM A RANGE OF SIX METERS, AND THE INK IS *SODIUM PENTATHOL.* WHOEVER YOU HIT WILL DO *EXACTLY* WHAT YOU TELL THEM FOR THE NEXT *SIX HOURS.*

BUT I'VE SAVED THE *BEST* 'TIL *LAST...*

SLIP IN THIS GAME, *CALLUP,* AND IT'S A *PDA SCANNER AND TRANSMITTER.* THAT'S HOW YOU KEEP IN *TOUCH* WITH US.

PANIC STATION IS A *BUG-FINDER* AND *SONIC INTENSIFIER.* YOU CAN HEAR A CONVERSATION *TWO ROOMS* AWAY.

THIS ONE IS CALLED *GREEN SCREEN.* IT TURNS THE WHOLE THING INTO A *SMOKE BOMB,* WITH A *FIVE SECOND* FUSE.

WHAT ABOUT *MARIO KART?*

OH, THAT'S JUST A *GAME.*

I THOUGHT YOU MIGHT LIKE IT FOR THE *FLIGHT.*

IT'S **OUTRAGEOUS!** I MEAN, EVEN THE **CIA** WOULDN'T COME UP WITH SOMETHING LIKE THIS!

WHAT AM I SAYING? OF COURSE THEY WOULD...

BUT IT'S OUT OF THE **QUESTION,** ALEX. YOU'RE **NOT GOING.** I KNOW WHAT **IAN** WOULD SAY...

IT WAS **HIS IDEA.**

CHELSEA

HE **LIED** TO ME, JACK.

ALL MY LIFE HE WAS **PREPARING** ME FOR THIS. EVERYTHING HE EVER DID... HE WAS JUST **MANIPULATING** ME.

YOU DON'T **KNOW** THAT, ALEX. HE NEVER **SAID** ANYTHING... MAYBE HE WAS TRYING TO **PROTECT** YOU.

NO. HE **KNEW.**

I DIDN'T KNOW WHETHER TO **SHOW** YOU THIS OR **NOT.**

IT CAME WHILE YOU WERE **AWAY.**

IT'S FROM **IAN.**

HE MUST HAVE POSTED IT BEFORE...

"WISH YOU WERE HERE WITH ME. THERE'S SO MUCH TO SEE."

IT'S FROM *CORNWALL!*

GREETINGS FROM CORNWALL

BUT HE DIDN'T MEAN YOU TO GO THERE *NOW*, ALEX. THAT'S NOT WHAT HE *MEANT*...

IT'S ONLY A FEW DAYS, JACK.

I'LL BE *CAREFUL.*

YOU REALLY *PROMISE* ME?

I PROMISE.

AND ALEX...

WHAT?

ANOTHER *GADGET?*

WHAT IS IT, A *LOCKPICK?* DOES IT *EXPLODE?*

NO, ALEX.

IT *CLEANS* YOUR *TEETH.*

MRS. VOLE, IS THAT RIGHT? I'M THE EDITOR OF *DISC DRIVE WORLD*...

THEN THIS MUST BE *KEVIN*, JA?

THAT'S ME.

KEVIN BLAKE!

GUT. YOU SHOULD SAY *GOODBYE* NOW.

GOODBYE, KEVIN! I HOPE YOU FIND YOUR STAY VERY *INFORMATIVE!*

← ARRIVAL

CAR PARK →

I'M SURE IT *WILL* BE...

I AM *NADIA VOLE.* I WORK FOR *MR. SAYLE* IN *PR.*

PUBLIC RELATIONS?

JA. THIS IS *PORT TALLON.* A *FISHING VILLAGE.*

PORT TALLON
Welcome
Careful Drivers

NICE PLACE.

NOT IF YOU ARE A *FISH.*

IT'S *NINETY-NINE PERCENT WATER*. IT HAS NO *BRAINS*, AND NO *ANUS*.

THE *MAN-OF-WAR* IS AN *OUTSIDER*.

IT'S *SILENT*, YET IT DEMANDS *RESPECT*. THOSE *TENTACLES* ARE COVERED IN *NEMATOCYSTS*... STINGING CELLS. IF YOU CAME INTO *CONTACT* WITH THEM, YOU'D DIE A VERY *MEMORABLE* DEATH.

I'M TOO *YOUNG* TO DIE.

...I THINK I'M GOING TO *LIKE* YOU.

NO, NO, *NO*. I WOULDN'T BELIEVE *THAT*.

YOU'RE *NEVER* TOO YOUNG TO DIE.

WHAT THE...?

IT SEEMS I'M *NOT* GOING TO BE ABLE TO *JOIN* YOU FOR LUNCH AFTER *ALL*, BUT I HOPE YOU'LL HAVE *DINNER* WITH ME TONIGHT.

HIYA, CUDDLES.

MR. SAYLE, THE *AMERICAN AMBASSADOR* IS ON LINE ONE.

FZZZZZzzzzz

IT'S BEEN QUITE A **WHILE** SINCE I FOUND MYSELF FACE-TO-FACE WITH A BRITISH **SCHOOLKID**... I CAN'T **WAIT** TO HEAR WHAT YOU THINK OF THE **STORMBREAKER**.

THIS IS MY PERSONAL ASSISTANT, **MR. GRIN**.

HE SEEMS TO HAVE **CUT** HIMSELF **SHAVING**.

MR. GRIN USED TO WORK IN A **CIRCUS**. IT WAS A NOVELTY **KNIFE-THROWING** ACT. FOR A **CLIMAX**, HE CAUGHT A **SPINNING KNIFE** BETWEEN HIS **TEETH**...

...UNTIL **ONE** NIGHT, HIS MOTHER **WAVED** TO HIM FROM THE FRONT ROW AND HE MADE A **MISTAKE** WITH HIS **TIMING**.

MURGH.

HE CAN'T **TALK**, BUT HE'LL SHOW YOU TO YOUR **ROOM** AND WE'LL MEET AGAIN **TONIGHT**. OKAY?

HAVE **FUN**.

BEEP

HMMM.

TIK!

SKEEEECH!

YAAAAAAA!

KNOCK
KNOCK

IT IS *TIME* FOR YOU TO SEE THE *STORMBREAKER.*

YOU ARE THE *FIRST* CHILD TO EXPERIENCE THE *POWER*, THE *WORLD DOMINATION* OF THE STORMBREAKER.

THIS MODEL HAS BEEN ALREADY LOADED WITH *HIGHLY DEVELOPED* PROGRAMS FOR ALL ASPECTS OF THE *SCHOOL CURRICULUM.*

SO, UM... WHERE *IS* IT?

YOU ARE *STANDING* IN IT. IT IS THE *STORMBREAKER PROTOTYPE.*

STEP ONTO THE *PLATFORM.*

DOES IT HAVE *PINBALL?*

BE *STILL*, PLEASE, WHILE WE *SCAN* YOU.

JA! WHO **TAUGHT** YOU ABOUT COMPUTERS, KEVIN?

YOU'RE USING **SLICE-MATRIX VIRTUAL REALITY** SOFTWARE, AREN'T YOU?

MY UNCLE.

HE IS A COMPUTER **WHIZ-KING**?

NO, HE WAS A **SECURITY GUARD.** BUT HE **DIED.**

HOW DID THAT **HAPPEN?**

I DON'T **KNOW.**

BUT **ONE** DAY I'LL FIND **OUT.**

PROGRAMMING COMPLETE

MAYBE.

BUT **NOT** TODAY.

YOU WILL START WITH **SCIENCE.** PRESS **ENTER** TO BEGIN.

SCIENCE, EH? GREAT...

...NOT.

UH-OH.

GOOD **MORNING**, MR. SAYLE.

IS IT **READY** FOR ME?

YES, SIR. THIS WAY, PLEASE...

...THE **BACK-UP** SYSTEM.

IT WILL SEND OUT A **SIGNAL** THAT WILL **INSTANTLY** ACTIVATE ALL **SEVENTY THOUSAND** COMPUTERS.

OF COURSE, IT SHOULDN'T BE **NEEDED.**

NO.

IT'S **EXCELLENT.** VERY—

—GOOD.

HMMM.

KEVIN?

DIESER **VERDAMMTE** JUNGE...

HMMM.

NICE **WEATHER** FOR THE TIME OF YEAR.

HOW WOULD *YOU* KNOW? WE HAVEN'T BEEN *TOPSIDE* IN *FORTY-EIGHT* HOURS.

I'M JUST TRYING TO MAKE *CONVERSATION.*

THIRTY-NINE HOURS TO FINAL DELIVERY.

WELL, *DON'T.*

ALL BE OVER *SOON*, ANYWAY.

THIRTY-NINE HOURS AND COUNTING...

KEVIN?

WHAT ARE YOU *DOING* DOWN HERE?

MISS VOLE! I... I JUST WONDERED WHERE THIS *WENT.*

WHAT *IS* THIS PLACE?

"THIS PLACE" IS *RESTRICTED.*

BITTE, *THIS* WAY!

...

I'D have said the same about YOU, Mr. Sayle.

GOOD POINT.

I'VE VERY MUCH ENJOYED MEETING YOU, KEVIN. I'M SURE YOU'LL HAVE A LOT TO TALK ABOUT WHEN YOU GET BACK TO SCHOOL.

SURE.

AND WHEN WE LAUNCH THE STORMBREAKERS TOMORROW...

I'LL BE THINKING PARTICULARLY OF YOU.

BRRRRING

CHELSEA

EXCUSE ME, FRÄULEIN.

I AM **LOOKING** FOR A PERSON CALLED **JACK**.

IS THIS ABOUT **ALEX?**

YES...

YES, IT **IS.**

THEN YOU'D BETTER COME **IN.**

YOU ARE A **FRIEND** OF ALEX?

I **LOOK AFTER** HIM.

THIS IS ALEX, YES? AND THIS **MAN** WITH HIM... HIS **FATHER?**

HIS **UNCLE!** LOOK, WHAT'S THIS **ABOUT?**

TELL ME...

WHO **IS** THIS BOY **ALEX RIDER?** WHAT IS HE **DOING?**

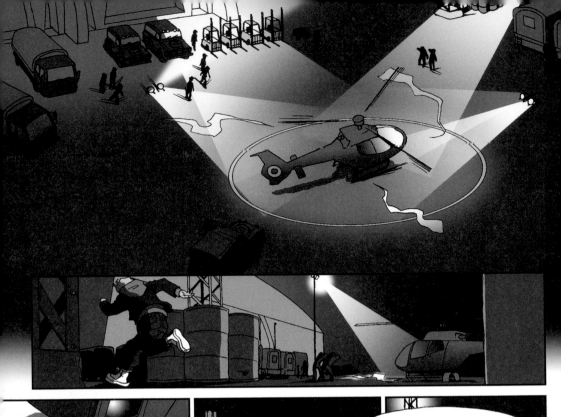

LET US START.

MR. GREGOROVICH!

I'M GLAD YOU WERE ABLE TO JOIN US TONIGHT.

I DIDN'T REALIZE YOU WERE GOING TO COME PERSONALLY.

I TOLD YOU I **DIDN'T** WANT TO BE **INTERRUPTED**...

...UNLESS IT WAS **IMPORTANT**.

AND **IS** IT?

LONDON

WE JUST GOT **THIS** FROM ALEX RIDER.

"GREGOROVICH"? **YASSEN** GREGOROVICH?

IT **HAS** TO BE.

I THOUGHT HE WAS STILL IN **NORTH KOREA**.

IT SEEMS **NOT**.

THIS IS THE **PROOF** YOU NEED, ALAN. THE STORMBREAKER **LAUNCH** IS LESS THAN **24 HOURS** AWAY. **CANCEL** IT.

YES. YOU'RE **RIGHT**.

I'LL PUT A **CALL** IN TO **DOWNING STREET**.

AND GET ALEX **OUT**.

HE'LL BE **FLYING** OUT AT TWELVE O'CLOCK TOMORROW **ANYWAY**. NO POINT MAKING SAYLE — OR **GREGOROVICH**, COME TO THAT — **SUSPICIOUS**.

YOU CAN **MEET** HIM IF YOU LIKE. TAKE HIM OUT FOR AN **ICE CREAM**.

WHAT?

HE'S DONE VERY **WELL**. HE DESERVES A **TREAT**.

SNAP.

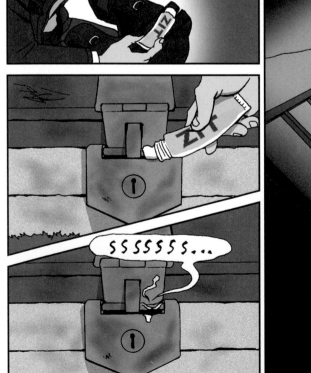

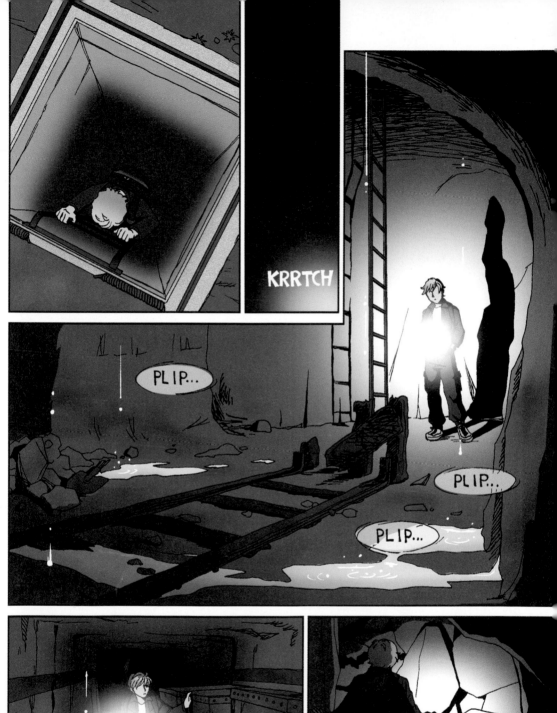

KRRTCH

PLIP...

PLIP...

PLIP...

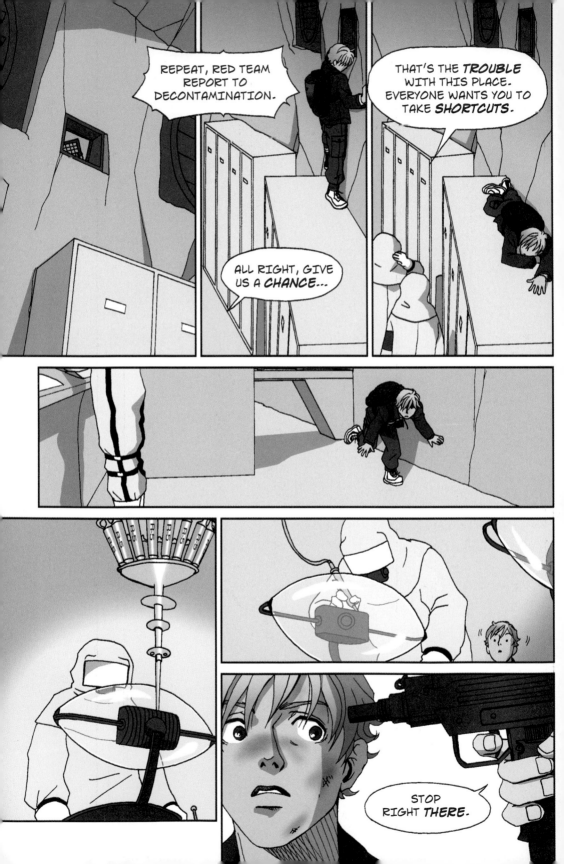

WHAT ARE YOU **DOING** HERE? WHO **ARE** YOU?

WHAT'S GOING **ON?** MY NAME'S **KEVIN BLAKE**... I WAS **INVITED** HERE.

IT IS A **GOOD ACT**. YOU DO IT VERY **WELL**. BUT YOU **SHOULDN'T** HAVE COME HERE.

WE CAN **TALK** ABOUT THIS...

I DO NOT **THINK** SO.

YES, WE **CAN!**

BE **CAREFUL!**

DO **NOT** DROP THAT...

"**R5.**" WHAT IS IT?

PUT IT **BACK**, "KEVIN."

ALL RIGHT, THEN... WHAT'S THE WAY **OUT** OF HERE?

GOING SOMEWHERE, MEIN JUNGE?

YEAH.

I HAVE A **PLANE** TO CATCH.

NOT ANY**MORE**.

WHAT'S YOUR **NAME**?

YOU **KNOW** WHO I AM. I WON THE **COMPETITION**.

SIGH

MR. GRIN?

THUNK

IF *THIS* IS HOW YOU TREAT THE *WINNER*, I'D *HATE* TO SEE WHAT HAPPENED TO THE *RUNNER-UP*.

YOU'RE *NOT* KEVIN BLAKE.

YOU'RE *ALEX RIDER*.

YOUR *UNCLE* WAS PRETENDING TO BE A *SECURITY* GUARD, BUT *YASSEN GREGOROVICH* DEALT WITH *HIM*...

...AND *MIG* SENT *YOU* TO TAKE HIS PLACE.

SENDING A *FOURTEEN-YEAR-OLD* TO DO THEIR *DIRTY WORK*. NOT VERY *BRITISH*, I'D HAVE SAID. NOT *CRICKET*.

WHAT ARE YOU *DOING* HERE? WE *KNOW* YOU'RE PUTTING SOME KIND OF *VIRUS* INTO THE STORMBREAKER...

OH! IT'S... IT'S NOT A *COMPUTER* VIRUS, IS IT?

IT'S *THE REAL THING!*

VERY *CLEVER*, ALEX.

IT'S CALLED *R5*... A *GENETICALLY MODIFIED* VIRUS.

IT'S *VERY* NASTY.

BUT YOU'LL KILL **THOUSANDS** OF PEOPLE!

WHAT?

NO, NO, DON'T BE **SILLY**.

I'LL KILL **MILLIONS** OF THEM.

ALL BECAUSE YOU WERE **BULLIED** AT **SCHOOL**?

LOTS OF PEOPLE ARE BULLIED AT SCHOOL, BUT IT DOESN'T TURN **THEM** INTO **RAVING PSYCHOPATHS!**

TIME TO SAY **GOODBYE**, ALEX.

AS YOU MAY HAVE SEEN, I'M **PACKING UP** AND **LEAVING**. I'D **LOVE** TO STAY, BUT I HAVE A RATHER IMPORTANT APPOINTMENT IN **LONDON**.

THUNK

SO I'LL LEAVE YOU TO **NADIA**.

THAT WAS... A GOOD **SHOT**.

EURGH.

ACTUALLY, IT WAS A **NEAR MISS**. YOU SHOULD WATCH YOUR **MOUTH**.

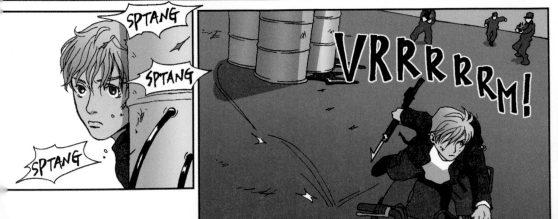

...FINAL DEPARTURE IS NOW. ALL PERSONNEL EVACUATE IMMEDIATELY.

REPEAT, FINAL DEPARTURE...

BOOM!

IMPRESSIVE.

NUUUH...

EUUGH!

ALL RIGHT, MR. GRIN.

I WANT YOU TO FLY ME TO *LONDON.* AS *FAST* AS YOU CAN.

YARGH...

HYDE PARK, LONDON

WE DON'T HAVE *TIME* FOR THIS NOW, MISS STARBRIGHT.

THE *PRIME MINISTER* IS...

WE DON'T KNOW.

WHAT DO YOU *MEAN*, YOU *DON'T KNOW?* YOU *PROMISED* ME YOU'D LOOK AFTER HIM!

LADIES AND GENTLEMEN, *THANK YOU.*

THE MESSAGE TODAY IS QUITE *CLEAR.*

CLAP

CLAP

CLAP

CLAP

"AND THAT MESSAGE IS *EDUCATION.* EDUCATION, EDUCATION,

AND..."

BROOKLAND SCHOOL

YOU CAN LEAVE HIM TO *US*. DON'T *WORRY* ABOUT HIM.

YOU'VE DONE VERY *WELL*, ALEX. BUT YOU SHOULD *GO*, NOW.

WHAT ABOUT *SAYLE?*

...FINE.

HOW COULD THEY LET HIM SLIP *AWAY?*

IT'S NOT YOUR *PROBLEM*. I CAN'T BELIEVE I *EVER* LET YOU GET *MIXED UP* IN ALL THIS.

BUT IT'S *OVER* NOW, AND IT'S TIME YOU CAME *HOME*.

YEAH, BUT WHERE'S HE *GOING...?*

JACK! STOP THE *CAR!*

SOMEWHERE *REMOTE* AND *FAR AWAY* WHERE NOBODY WILL *EVER* FIND HIM. LIKE... *PARAGUAY*.

OR *IOWA*.

THAT'S IT!

SAYLE TOWER!

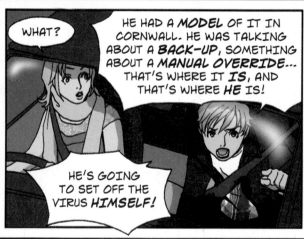

WHAT?

HE HAD A **MODEL** OF IT IN CORNWALL. HE WAS TALKING ABOUT A **BACK-UP**, SOMETHING ABOUT A **MANUAL OVERRIDE**... THAT'S WHERE IT **IS**, AND THAT'S WHERE **HE** IS!

HE'S GOING TO SET OFF THE VIRUS **HIMSELF**!

COME **ON**, PUT YOUR **FOOT** DOWN!

I CAN'T!

WHY **NOT?** JACK, HE'LL KILL **EVERYONE**!

BECAUSE, ALEX, YOU'RE NOT IN **CORNWALL** ANYMORE.

WELCOME TO **LONDON TRAFFIC**.

NO...

ALEX?

ALEX, WHAT ARE YOU *DOING?*

I HAVE TO *STOP* HIM, JACK! I'LL *RUN* THERE IF—

ALEX?

WHAT ARE *YOU* DOING HERE?

SABINA...?

I THOUGHT YOU HAD *MUMPS.*

I GOT *BETTER.*

LOOK, SABINA, I NEED YOUR *HELP.* I HAVE TO BE ON THE *OTHER* SIDE OF *LONDON,* RIGHT *NOW!*

WHY?

I...

HAVE TO *SAVE* THE *WORLD?*

OH, OK.

...

THAT'S RIGHT, **MRS. JONES!**

I DON'T **KNOW** WHAT HER **FIRST NAME** IS! I'M NOT SENDING HER A **BIRTHDAY** CARD, THIS IS **URGENT!** STOP MAKING ME—

—JUMP OVER HURDLES...

YAAAH!

ALEX...

KEEP GOING!

AAAAH!

WOOOAH!

HEY, YASSEN! ABOUT TIME!

WASTE THESE KIDS FOR ME, WOULD YOU?

DO YOU *TRUST* ME?

NO!

TYPICAL.

!

HOLD **ON**...

AAAAAAH!

TWANG

UNH!

TWANG

PING

SAYLE HAD BECOME AN *EMBARRASSMENT* TO THE PEOPLE I *WORK* FOR.

WHAT ABOUT *ME?*

I HAVE NO *INSTRUCTIONS* CONCERNING YOU.

THIS DOESN'T *CHANGE* ANYTHING. YOU *KILLED* MY *UNCLE.* YOU'RE STILL MY *ENEMY.*

I HAVE *MANY* ENEMIES.

THIS *ISN'T OVER,* GREGOROVICH!

I THINK IT *IS,* ALEX. GO BACK TO *SCHOOL.*

YOU DO NOT *BELONG* TO MY WORLD, AND YOU SHOULD *FORGET* ABOUT ME.

I'LL *NEVER* FORGET YOU.

THAT IS *YOUR* CHOICE.

BROOKLAND SCHOOL

This book has been typeset in Lint McCree.

Screenplay © MMVI Samuelsons / IoM Film.
Film © MMVI Film & Entertainment VIP Medienfonds 4 GmbH & Co. KG.
Style Guide © MMVI ARR Ltd. Graphic Novelisation by Antony Johnston.
Illustrated by Kanako and Yuzuru.
Trademarks 2006 Samuelson Productions Ltd.
Stormbreaker™, Alex Rider™, Boy with torch logo™, AR logo™.

Text and illustrations copyright © 2006 by Walker Books Ltd.
Based on the original novel Stormbreaker © 2000 by Anthony Horowitz.
All rights reserved. Published by Scholastic Inc.,
557 Broadway, New York, NY 10012,
by arrangement with Penguin Group (USA) Inc.
Printed in the U.S.A.

ISBN-13: 978-0-545-33964-3
ISBN-10: 0-545-33964-2

1 2 3 4 5 6 7 8 9 10   40
20 19 18 17 16 15 14 13 12 11

ANTHONY HOROWITZ,
who scripted the movie blockbuster
STORMBREAKER from his own
novel, is one of the most popular
and prolific children's writers
working today. His hugely
successful Alex Rider series
has won numerous awards and
sold over eight million copies
worldwide. He has won the
Red House Children's Book
Award on two occasions, in
2003 for SKELETON KEY and
in 2006 for ARK ANGEL. He also
writes extensively for TV, with
programs including MIDSOMER
MURDERS, POIROT and FOYLE'S
WAR. He is married to television
producer Jill Green and lives in
north London with his two sons,
Nicholas and Cassian, and their
dog, Lucky.

www.anthonyhorowitz.com

ANTONY JOHNSTON,
who wrote the script for this
book, is the author of nine graphic
novels, including THE LONG HAUL,
JULIUS, THREE DAYS IN EUROPE
and ROSEMARY'S BACKPACK, and
the ongoing series WASTELAND.
He has also adapted many prose
works by Alan Moore into comics
form, and is the only other writer
to have penned a story for Greg
Rucka's award-winning QUEEN &
COUNTRY series. Antony lives in
northwest England with the three
loves of his life; his partner Marcia,
his dog Connor, and his iMac.

www.mostlyblack.com

The artwork in this graphic
novel is the work of two artists,
KANAKO DAMERUM and
YUZURU TAKASAKI, who
collaborate on every illustration.
Although living on opposite
sides of the globe, these Japanese
sisters work seamlessly together
via the Internet.

Living and working in Tokyo,
YUZURU produced all the line
work for these illustrations using
traditional means. The quality of
her draftsmanship comes from
years of honing her skills in the
highly competitive world of manga.

KANAKO lives and works out of
her studio in London. She managed
and directed the project as well
as coloring and rendering the
artwork digitally using her wealth
of knowledge in graphic design.

www.manga-media.com
www.thorogood.net

Date Due	Borrower's Name